To The Gravinese Kids -
Remember to listen.
Sue + Phil
☺

To Amanda Rose. Thank you for every heart you have shared with me.

ImperfectPhil is Kind!
Author: Sue Steinhardt
Illustrations: Jessica Murr
Interior Layout: Michael Nicloy
Spanish Translation: Natalia Jaramillo

Hardcover ISBN: 979-8-9890505-9-8

Published by BC Books, LLC
Franklin, Wisconsin
Brenda E. Cortez, Publisher
Jean Sime, Publishing Coordinator

www.bcbooksllc.com
Quantity orders can be emailed to:
info@bcbooksllc.com

Printed in The United States of America

IMPERFECTPHIL IS KIND!

Sue Steinhardt

Illustrated by Jessica Murr

I love to go for a walk and spend time with my friends.

We hike in the cold when it's snowing, walk in the wet when it's raining, and enjoy the heat when the sun is shining.

When we are out walking, we chase squirrels, carry sticks, jump in puddles, and run zoomies all around.

When we go for a walk, we have time to clear our minds and think about the day.

Sometimes, we walk in silence, lost in our thoughts, or talk about how to make our dreams come true.

It makes me happy to listen.

What are your dreams?

When I get excited, I jump in my tracks and give my friends an enthusiastic wiggle.

When my friends are silly, I stop where I am
and show them my best "Are you joking?" look

If someone gets sad, I tug on my leash, wrap around their legs, and offer them my most sincere, "it will be okay" eyes.

I offer comfort and do my best to be a friend.

After all, we are buddies!

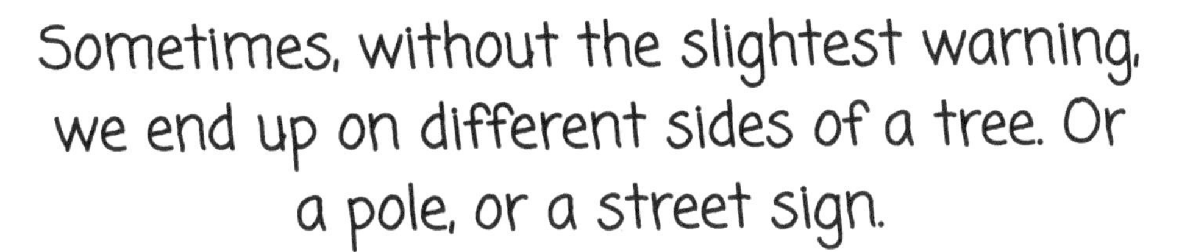

Sometimes, without the slightest warning, we end up on different sides of a tree. Or a pole, or a street sign.

Somehow, I go left, and they go right...or I go right, and they go left...and there we have it—tangled.

Separated. Split apart.

Despite our best efforts, this problem is common.

We stop and look at each other and try to figure out what has happened.

I tug on my end of the leash
and my pals pull on theirs.

We are stuck on different sides of what is between us.

No one ever wins this kind of tug-of-war.

Being divided makes me sad.
I don't want to lose a good friend.

Happily, we are still connected.
The leash always holds us together.

So we work as a team.

What does teamwork look like to you?

We decide it is best to sit still and be patient.

If we take a few steps back and figure out where we went wrong, we can choose a different path forward.

If we see each other, hear each other, and respect each other, we will be on our way again.

What matters most is that we are side-by-side, on a walk, with time to talk about how to make our dreams come true.

I'm a dog, I love life, and I have flaws. I'm perfect.
Imperfect.
Just. Like. You.

ABOUT THE AUTHOR

Sue Steinhardt is a retired high school English teacher with the simple philosophy of "be". She grew up in Belvidere, New Jersey, and still lives nearby with her husband and furbabies. Sue loves walking in the woods and sharing a laugh about the quirks of life with good friends. She loves dogs, believes in rescues, always recycles, drinks from a reusable straw, and tries to breathe deeply rather than act harshly. She is not perfect.

To stay in touch, follow Sue's blog at imperfectphil.com. Check out Phil on Instagram @imperfect_phil and Twitter @imperfectphil1. Follow Phil Basher on Facebook.

ABOUT THE ARTIST

Jessica Murr is a graduate of Savannah College of Art and Design where she received her Bachelor of Fine Arts degree. Jess hopes to spread her artwork around the world and make a positive impact. She grew up in Mt. Olive, New Jersey, where she began her art career. There, she was able to grow and develop into the artist that she is today with the help of her family, friends, teachers, and furry companions. One of her biggest goals is to better the life of those around her. You can follow her journey through the art world on Instagram @jessilynneart

Sue and Jess first met as teacher and student, and their journey to ImperfectPhil is proof of how important those relationships are.

Printed in the USA
CPSIA information can be obtained
at www.ICGtesting.com
JSHW070801080624
64322JS00002B/3